FOLK SONGS OF CHINA, JAPAN, KOREA

Folk songs are the loved songs of the world. Only because they are loved have they survived. They were the newspapers of yesteryear, carrying tales of war and peace, love and hate, social customs and intrigue. They remain even today bearers of tradition and messengers of sorrow and joy, hope and despair, and the beauty of nature, especially among people who have no book learning.

That is why the folk songs in this volume have been loved by whole communities of Chinese, Japanese, and Korean people. Betty Dietz and Thomas Choonbai Park have assembled and arranged them because Oriental folk songs are so little known to Westerners. The American soldier serving in Korea probably learned to sing the famous "Arirang"; but he was exposed to few others and his countrymen are mostly unacquainted even with that one.

Featuring:
    Simple piano accompaniments in the pentatonic mode
    Lyrics in both English and Oriental characters
    Notes on pronunciation
    Reference materials in the Appendix

FOLK SONGS of
CHINA
JAPAN
KOREA

EDITED BY BETTY WARNER DIETZ
AND THOMAS CHOONBAI PARK

ENGLISH VERSIONS OF FOREIGN LYRICS BY
THOMAS CHOONBAI PARK AND BETTY WARNER DIETZ

PIANO ARRANGEMENTS BY BETTY WARNER DIETZ

THE JOHN DAY COMPANY · NEW YORK

ACKNOWLEDGMENTS

Special mention of sincere appreciation is made to the following:

Dr. and Mrs. Sankey C. Chao for their contribution of Chinese songs.

Mr. Eugene Langston, Executive Director of The Japan Society, who helped the editors secure tape recordings of Japanese songs, checked the accuracy of the historical and geographic facts, and corrected the romanization of the Japanese lyrics.

The Japan Broadcasting Corporation and the Korean Research and Information Service for their permission to transcribe and publish songs from the tape recordings they sent us.

The many Asian students at the University of Florida who provided background material and patiently sang songs over and over as Thomas Choonbai Park transcribed and translated them.

Dr. Thomas Tao Cheng for his assistance in translating the Chinese songs and in developing the phonetic pronunciation.

Dr. Mary Yui, who checked and simplified the phonetic form of the Chinese lyrics.

Charity Bailey for her continued moral support and encouragement, for writing the accompaniment to one song, and for frequent criticism of the other piano arrangements.

Henrietta Yurchenco for reviewing the piano arrangements.

Dr. Henry Cowell for his critique of the first draft of the manuscript.

Photograph Credits:

Chinese News Service
Japan Airlines
The New York Times

Library of Congress Catalogue Card Number: 64-14209 Manufactured in the United States of America

TO

Jingoo, Suejong, Jinoh, Sueduk, and Suegyong Park and to all North Americans who sincerely wish to become better acquainted with their Asian brothers, especially Peggy, Laura, and John Rea.

PREFACE

So varied are the folk songs of the world that it may appear impossible to know all the varieties, yet so beautiful are they that we must explore. The folk songs in this book were loved by whole communities of Chinese, Japanese, and Korean people. Some, like "Blue Bird" and "The Hakone Mountain Road," have survived for centuries, carrying in their lyrics historical records which otherwise might be lost among people who had no "book learning." Some teach social customs, for children learn their patterns of living from their elders, and the folk, even today, are singing people. China, Japan, and Korea are nations of farmers and fishermen, miners and soldiers. They are nations where poverty is common, where, over the ages, wars have been fought again and again. Their people sing of sorrows and joys, love and hope, work and play, and the beauties of nature.

The folk songs of the world are the loved songs of the world. Only because they are loved have they survived. We in the United States sing fondly the songs of our founding fathers — the folk songs of western Europe. The Negro contributed some of our most moving songs when he created the spirituals, built on his African heritage. Songs were born during the Revolutionary and Civil Wars, others emerged as pioneers made their way to the Pacific. Mountain tunes, sea chanteys, cowboy songs, and tunes of farmers and lumbermen appeared from nowhere and were remembered only as people learned them from one another in an oral tradition. Folk songs were the newspapers of yesterday, carrying tales of war and peace, love and hate, social customs, murder and intrigue.

The songs of the Slavic and Latin-American countries are now being absorbed into our many-hued cultural fabric, but few Oriental songs are known in this country as yet. The American G.I. serving in Korea probably learned to sing "Arirang," the best-loved of all Korean folk songs, but he was exposed to few other Asian folk songs. We who served as technical experts learned many Korean folk songs and, in turn, taught the Korean people many of our favorites. It was amusing to hear "Clementine" sung lustily in Korean and to learn that it had been loved for so many years that some were unaware of its American origin.

Such is the growth of a folk song! Origins are forgotten. Changes in melody, rhythm, and words develop as the song passes orally from one group to another. Now that transportation and communication have so shrunk our world, the best-loved songs of every nation will be sung in the languages of other nations. In fact, in recent years, anthropologists and musicologists have made determined efforts to collect and record the folk music of the world before its original flavor is lost. Field recordings preserve one version of a song as it is being sung, but we must remember that a folk song always has more than one version. We must expect to find each song in several variations.

One verse of each song in the book is written in the phonetic form of the Chinese, Japanese, or Korean text so that it may be learned in its original language. Singing the same song with its English lyrics will increase understanding. Students of Oriental languages will find each song written in its original characters, also.

The realities of today's world demand that North Americans learn more about their brothers in other countries, particularly those in Asia. Only through knowing them can we learn to appreciate them and to become friends. One way of becoming acquainted is to sing their songs, so sing your way joyously through this book. What we learn and take to heart as children is reflected in our actions when we grow up. The social and political behavior of tomorrow's citizens may be influenced for the better through contact with each other, both vicariously and actually.

The world marches forward on the feet of little children.

B. W. D.

Baldwin, New York
June, 1964

CONTENTS

Included in the book is a long-playing record (33⅓ R.P.M.) of authentic renditions of a selection of the songs.

CHINESE FOLK SONGS

WHY DON'T YOU COME HOME?
(Wei Sha Bu Hwei Ja)

There always has been a great contrast between the rich and the poor in China. Poor families cannot grow enough food to feed all mouths, therefore the son mentioned in this song left home to find work elsewhere. His father is worried, for he has not written. Often, when a son leaves home in this manner, he wanders from place to place, never putting down any roots. This is contrary to the Chinese tradition of maintaining the family unit.

Szechwan Province, China

Slowly and sadly

I think of my son when the moon goes down. Oh, my thought-less
Ywe ur le shi shia sze shung shao yuen ja. Yuen ___ ja ta

way-ward boy, you have sent no news. I am wor-ried ov-er you.
i ___ chu, wu ___ yin ___ shin. Shin li lon ru ma.

為 啥 不 回 家
四川民歌
月兒落西斜, 思想小冤家.
冤家他一去 無音信. 心里乱如麻.

THE VAGABOND'S SONG
(Lio Lang Jr Ge)

Perhaps the vagabond who sings this gay song is a poor man who had to leave his family in search of work, like the son in the previous song. Shinchiang Province is far from the sea. Great, wide plains stretch endlessly with no mountains in sight.

Shinchiang Province

Vigorously, in march rhythm

One can- not walk to the ho - ri — zon, Plains stretch end-less-ly a - head.
Zo bbu ddao de tien — pien yo. ——— Zo bbu jing de pin — yuan.

Heav - en lies be - yond the plains, Plains lie 'neath the rim of heav'n.
Tien bien di sha shr pin yuan. Pin yuan gwo chu shr tien bien.

2. It is warm when the sun rises,
   Moonlight casts a silver glow.
   Oh, to be a vagabond!
   This is just the life for me!

流　浪　之　歌
新疆民歌
走不到的天边哟，　走不盡的平原．
天边底下是平原，　平原過去是天边．

14

FROGS
(Show Ha Mo)

"Frogs," like "Welcome Spring," expresses the people's wish for
peace. This counting song may be sung as a round. Notice that there is
a pause for breath at the end of each phrase of two measures. Exag-
gerate this somewhat. Play the song on the black keys of the piano or
on the song bells (xylophone type, chromatic) to illustrate the five-tone
scale. Start on D-flat and flat each note in turn.

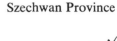

Briskly and lightly

1. Each frog has a sin-gle mouth. He has two eyes and four legs.
   Yi jr ha mo yi jang zwei. Lyang jr yan jin sz tiao tuei.

3. Pin pong pin pong Count them _ with me. Dur-ing time of peace frogs do not drink.
   Teo sha _ shui ya. Ha mo bu chr shue tai pin _ nyan.

5. Dur-ing time of peace frogs do not drink. Wa-ter li-lies float on the pond.
   Ha mo bu chr shue tai pin _ nyan. He ur mei tz shi shuei shang pyao.

數 蛤蟆

四川民歌

一只蛤蟆 一張嘴 兩只眼睛四條腿.

乒乒乒乒 跳下水呀.

蛤蟆不吃水 太平年, 蛤蟆不吃水 太平年

荷兒梅子兮 水上漂, 花兒梅子兮 水上漂

WELCOME SPRING
(Yin Chuin Wha Ur Kai)

The history of China has been one of constant conflict. Confucius once said, "A person who invents instruments to kill people is evil." The Chinese people, like people everywhere, hate war. This song expresses their wish that the joys of peace, which they liken to the beauty and happiness of springtime, will be with them forever.

Shansi Province

迎 春 花 兜 開

山 西 民 歌

人人那了 都把喲. 春天愛.

世界的和平 不能破坏.

人人呀都把 和平愛. 哎嗨喲.

和平的春天 永久的在, 哎嗨喲.

16

POOR SZ BBEI
(Sz Bbei Shang Gung)

Sz Bbei is a laborer who works on a farm near Peiping, north of the
Yellow River. Even on New Year's Day poor Sz Bbei has no holiday!

Hopei Province

Moderately, with sympathy

On ___ New Year's Day, Sz Bbei has to work, Farm-er Sz
Jen ___ ywe ___ li, Jen ___ ywe ___ jen, Zo huo dde

Bbei has to work, ___ has to work. He car-ries bar-rels of
Sz Bbei ___ lai ___ shang ___ gung. Shang gung la shien tiao ___

wa-ter to the cat-tle, ___ *ya ur yo.* He cleans the
liang ___ ddan ___ shuei ya ba, ya ur yo. Chr wan le

cat-tle ___ sheds ___ af-ter break-fast. *Yi ur ya ur yo.*
zao fan ___ sao ___ nyo ___ pong. _____

四貝上工

河北民歌

正月裡 正月正， 做活的四貝來上工.

上工啦 先挑 兩担水呀吧 呀兒喲.

吃完了 早飯 掃牛棚， 伊兒 呀兒喲.

BAD FAITH
(Whai Lyang Shin)

For centuries, marriages were arranged by parents while their children were quite young. A daughter did not leave her father's home until she was old enough to live with her husband. Then, with great ceremony, the groom came to claim his bride and took her to the home of his parents, where they became part of the larger family unit. This song tells the feelings of folks whose friends failed to arrange their daughter's marriage. To add a second verse, change only the first line. Sing, "Such a great big window, such a great big door —"

Kansu Province

Lightly

Such a ve - ry big girl, such a fine young la - dy,
Jei me da de gu nyang, jei me da de jen,___

Such a charm - ing, love - ly big girl not yet
Jei me da de gu nyang bu a chia -

mar - ried! Her folks have ___ bad faith, bad faith.
jen.___ Nyang chia jen ___ whai le lyang shin.

Ai yo ao ai yo ao They should ar- range a prop-er mar- riage for her.
Nyang chia - jen - - - whai le lyang shin.

壞 良 心

甘肅民歌

這麼大的 姑娘 這麼大的人，

這麼大的 姑娘 不啊嫁人，

娘家人 坏了良心．

哎喲噢 哎喲噢，娘家人 坏了良心．

18

COOL BREEZES
(Liang Fung Lyao Lyao)

This song is sung by a river fisherman who appears to be having very bad luck. He throws his nets skillfully into the water and, time after time, hauls them in almost empty. After many hours, he folds his nets and leaves for home.

Szechwan Province

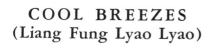

Very slowly

Soft cool breez-es__ help us sing,_____

Liang fung lyao lyao__ hao chang ge,_____

Wealth-y fam'-lies have ma-ny__ girls._____ Rich boys find wives__ eas-i-

Dda hu jen ja- jr mei__ dwo._____ Yo chien ge tz__ tao-i-

ly,_____ Man-y poor boys can-not_____ wed._____

ge,_____ Wu chien ge tz mei nai_____ ho._____

Copyright 1964 by The John Day Company, Inc.

2. Brilliant moonlight floods the sky,
   Cheers the fisherman as he works,
   Poor luck follows him all night.
   He goes home, so tired and sad!

涼 風 繞 繞

四川民歌

涼風繞繞 好唱歌, 大戶人家 姊妹多.

有錢哥子 討一个, 無錢哥子 沒奈何.

SONG OF THE THREE "NOTS"
(San Wu Yao)

Picture beautiful, rugged mountains lush with vegetation as you sing this song. Rushing mountain streams plunge down over the rocks with such speed that they seem to have little water in them. The natives are miners in peacetime and soldiers in time of war. Whether miners or soldiers, they are poor people.

The title calls attention to three facts: 1) not three miles in this mountainous region are on level ground; 2) the annual rainfall is so great that three days rarely pass without a downpour; and 3) no one has so much as three pennies.

Kwei Cho Province

Briskly

Kwei Cho's moun-tains are so high, Love-ly green_ moun-tains ris - ing_ sharp-ly.
Gwei Cho shan dwo yo dwo lin, Shan_ shan_ lin lin chin - yo _ chin ah.

For - ests grow on east and west slopes, Not_ three_ miles are on __ flat_ ground.
Dun shan jung shuh shi shan lin,___ Ung_ shr _ ddi wu san __ li __ pin.

Ke tong ke tong tong tong, Ke tong ke tong tong tong. Ke tong ke tong tong tong.

2. Kwei Cho's mountains are so high,
   Moss-covered mountains rising sharply,
   Pouring rain fills rushing streams,
   Not three days pass without rain.
   Ke tong ke tong tong tong,
   Ke tong ke tong tong tong.

3. Kwei Cho's mountains are so high,
   Tall, green mountains rich with min'rals,
   Mountain folk are soldiers or miners,
   Not even one man has three cents.
   Ke tong ke tong tong tong,
   Ke tong ke tong tong tong,
   Ke tong ke tong tong tong.

三　無　謠

貴州民歌

貴州山多又多嶺，山山嶺嶺青又青阿。

東山種樹西山林，硬是地無三里平。

可咚可咚咚咚，可咚可咚咚咚。

GENTLY FLOWING STREAM
(Shao Hua Tang Shui)

Every country has its love songs. This one flows as gently as a mountain brook.

Yunnan Province

Very slowly

Ai!

Ra - diant moon-beams bright-en the _ heav-ens tonight,
Ywe lyang chu lai lyang wang wang_ lyang wang wang,

I dream of my sweet-heart in the moon light.
Shang chi wo de a mei zai _ sheng _ shun.

I see her clear im-age in the moon's _ path. Sweet - heart,
Mai shyang ywe lyang tien shung zo _ tien shung zo. Mei gga

dear, _ dear, _ Ti - ny stream flows gent-ly in the for-est_ glen.
mei, _ mei, _ Shan sha shou he tang shui chin _ yo _ yo.

JAPANESE FOLK SONGS

AIZU LULLABY
(Aizu Komori Uta)

The Aizu District of Japan is known for the scenic beauty of its mountains, lakes, and valleys. It is here that this lovely lullaby is sung in the local dialect by young people who repeat it monotonously to put the baby to sleep. The same melody is sung to different words throughout the nation and often it is adapted to popular songs.

Fukushima Prefecture
(Arranged by Charity Bailey.)

Slowly and soothingly

Hi ya!— Go to — sleep,— ba - by,— Hi ya!— Go to — sleep.————
Ho ra — nei ro — nen — nei ro,— Ho ra — nei ro — ya.————

Go to — sleep my sweet — ba - by, Hi ya!— Go to — sleep.————
Nen —— nei ro nen —— nei ro, Ho ra — nei ro — ya.————

2. Nurse has gone to visit her fam'ly,
   She will bring them joy.
   When she returns to you, my baby,
   She will bring you a toy.

會津　子守唄

福島縣

オラ ネロ　ネンネロ　ホラネロヤ.

ネンネロ　ネンネロ　ホラネロヤ.

MISCANTHUS MOWING SONG
(Kariboshi Kiri Uta)

This work song provides rhythm for mowing the "kaya" or miscanthus, a wild grass of the reed family which grows as tall as a man in the hilly regions of Japan. It is used to thatch roofs and to feed farm animals. "Kariboshi" means drying the "kaya," and "kiru," a Kyushu expression, means mowing the grass with long-handled sickles.

The grass is dried in the sun after mowing and later is harvested. The farmers sing as they work independently,

far apart. Between verses they shout to each other, making plans for the evening's recreation. Their high-pitched voices echo in the valley under the crystal blue sky of autumn.

This song is sung in a slow tempo with the use of decorative notes, for the motion of mowing with long-handled sickles is slow and swaying. Listen to the recording to become familiar with the tempo of the song and its melody. We have written it in a lower key and have simplified the ornamentation of the melody to make singing easier.

Miyazaki Prefecture

2. The sun has sunken low.
   The sun will sink in the West.
   My little colt,
   You will carry hay on your back.

カリボシ　キリ　ウタ

ムコウノ　ヤマノ　カリボシ　ツンダヨ,

アスハ　タンボデ,　エ,　イネ　カロ　カヨ.

MAKING RICE CAKES
(Mochi Tauki Odori)

Rice cakes are eaten on such holidays as New Year's Day, Girls' Day (the third day of the third month), Boys' Day (the fifth day of the fifth month), and Bon Day, a harvest festival. Rice cakes are made from steamed rice which is mashed with a four-foot-high pestle in a three-foot-high mortar. When the mashed rice has been formed into cakes, some are eaten immediately. Others are dried and kept to be toasted later. Fancier cakes are made by rolling some in yellow bean powder and sugar and others in cooked black beans.

This work song provides rhythm for the pounding as the girls and boys help mash the huge quantities of rice. Young and old alike dance around the huge mortar, singing and pounding in time to the music. Toward the end this be-

comes a counting song. Enjoy the repetition of the Japanese sounds. Note that the word which follows each number in verses 2 through 10 begins with the same phonetic sound as the name of the number. (Ni nikkori, mittsu migotona, yottsu yononaka, etc.)

Learn to count from one to ten as you sing the song. There are two ways of counting in Japanese. One is based on Chinese, one is pure Japanese. The Chinese form is chi, ni, san, si, go, roku, sichi, hachi, ku, ju. The Japanese form is hitotsu, futatsu, mittsu, yottsu, itsutsu, muttsu, nanatsu, yattsu, kokonotsu, to. Notice that, in this song, the two forms are used — one (chi) and two (ni) being from the Chinese and the others from the Japanese. A single line repeats each time the counting song is sung.

Nara Prefecture

Come Ji - ro - yan, come Ta - ro - yan, Come with me and dance.
Ji - ro-yan- mo Ta - ro-yan- mo O - do-ri - an - sho.

Moth - er soon will join the par - ty, Come with me and dance.
Ya - ga - tei ka - ka-san- mo ku - ru - ja - ro.

Come with me and dance. Oh, 1. Raise your voic - es to the
O - do - ri - an - sho. O - ba ko ya - ma - ni to - do -
2. ro - sy sink - ing sun has
ka - i - hi o - chi -

skies, to O - ba - ko _____ moun - tain, Ho - i! Fac - es gleam with
kei, O - no - no _____ to, _____ Ho - i! Yu - hi ni
set and it's time to go home, _____ Ho - i! See the flick - 'ring
tei, O - i - ra - wa ka - e ru _____ Ho - i! Su - gi - no ya -

ro - sy glow to re - flect the sink - ing sun. _____
ya - kei - ru o - i - ra - no ka - o. _____
lan - tern lights shin - ing on the moun - tain top. _____
ma a - i - hi - ga to - mo - ru. _____ E n e _____ to -

o, o _____ ko - rya - sa. E _____ E _____

to o sa na _____ i yo sa. _____ Ah, the _____ ko - rya.
A, _____

(Counting song)

One, ___ let us car - ry rice to make de - li - cious rice cakes, ___
I - chi - de ta - wa - ra - o fun - ma - e - te, _____

Sa _____ e _____ na - i - yo sa ko - rya.

2. Two, let's be hap - py and have smil-ing fac-es,
   Ni - de nikk - o - ri - wa - ro -te,

3. Three, let us make some wishes for an am-ple har-vest,
   Mit - tsu mi - ga - to-na to-ri-i -ri -o,

4. Four, let us strug-gle to im-prove our ways of liv-ing,
   Yot - tsu yo - no-na-ka a - ra-ta - me-i tei,

5. Five, let's re-mem-ber to be hon'ra-ble and gen'rous,
   Itsu- tsu i - ta -wa-ru ko - ka - ro -dei,

6. Six, let us wish our vil-lage e'er to thrive and prosper,
   Mut-tsu mu - ra-wa yu - ta - ka-ni,

7. Seven, let's join hands in friendship, ev'ry one be joy-f[u]
   Na - na - tsu na - ka -ma - no u-de i o -r[i]

8. Eight, let us sing our dit-ties e'ven in the mountains,
   Yat - tsu ya - ma-ni-mo wu - ta-go- ei -o,

9. Nine, let our chil-dren grow strong and health-y,
   Ko-ko-no -tsu ko - do - mo-mo s'ko- ya- ka -ni,

10. Ten, let's work hard to make our wish-es all come true,
    To - de to - do-ka - sei ko - no-ne - gai,

11. Now, let's sing one more verse to bring us all good fortur[e]
    Mo-hi-to- tsu o - ma- ke - ni u - ta-wa-u - sho,

モチツキ オドリ

奈良縣

ジロヤンモ タロヤンモ オドリャンショ.

ヤガテ カカサンモ クルジャロウ, オドリャンショ.

オバコヤマニ トドケ オノオト "ホイ."

ユウヒニ ヤケル オイラノカヲ,

エンエト コリャサ, エ エト オサナイヨサ.

アカイヒ オケテ オイラハ カヘル, "ホイ."

スギノヤマ アイヒガ トモル.

エンエト コリャサ, エ エト オサナイヨサ, "コリャ."

イチデ タハララ フンマエテ

サエ ナイヨサ コリャ.

TO THE SEA GULL OFFSHORE
(Okino Kamomeini)

When a large shoal of herring is discovered offshore, fishermen board a fleet of boats and row out to the huge dragnet which was set into the sea earlier. Encircling the net with their boats, the men stand on board and pull up the net rhythmically as they sing this song. Sometimes men beat their boathooks on the sides of the boats in time to the music. When the dragnet has been pulled close to the boats, the fish are scooped on deck with smaller spoon-shaped nets which have handles about twenty-five feet long. Later, the fish are loaded into transports and are taken to market.

This is a call-and-response work song. A senior fisherman sings a phrase and the group joins in singing the nonsense syllables in a chorus. Then the elder sings another phrase and again the group sings a chorus. You will enjoy singing this as they did, or you may sing it in unison. Beat time with rhythm instruments — clapping sticks of some sort — just as the fishermen beat the rhythm on the sides of their boats with boathooks.

Hokkaido Prefecture

オキノ　カモメニ

北海道

オキノ　カモメニ　シオドキ　キケバ, ノエ,

ワタシャ　タツトリ, ヤッコラ　サノサ,

トコヤン　トコセ, ナミニ　キケバ, トコズイズイ

SONG OF THE CATTLE DRIVER
(Nambu Ushioi Uta)

Nambu is the name of a district in Iwate Prefecture in northern Japan. In feudal times it included part of Aomori Prefecture as well. Nambu District has long been noted as a cattle- and horse-breeding center, although in olden times it was a famous gold-mining region.

The cattle driver sings this song while descending a long solitary mountain path leading to the city where a fair is being held. As he walks at the rear of his herd, he directs the cattle in a novel manner. Whenever there is a turn in the path he uses a stick to poke the cow that is last in line. If the turn is left, he pokes the left side of the cow. If the turn is right, he pokes the right side of the cow. Each cow in turn "passes on" the signal by poking the one preceding it. The head cow, upon receiving the signal, turns correctly and leads the cattle down the trail.

Iwate and Aomori Prefectures

2. Rabbits jump in Shinano,
   Rabbits grow fat in farming country.
   Bunnies young learn to leap far,
   Learn to leap far as their parents,
       Sansai.

Long ago in Nambu,
These mountains once were noted for gold.
To the West and to the East
Miners dug gold from these mountains,
    Sansai.

ナンブ　ウシオイ　ウタ

岩手・青森縣、

イナカ　ナレドモ　ナンブノ　クニハ，サ，

ニシモ　ヒガシモ　カゲノ　イワマクラ，サンサイ．

HOHAI SONG
(Hohai Bushi)

"Hohai Bushi" is sung by farmers while working in the rice paddies or while dancing at the Bon Festival in celebration of a good harvest. This song is unique among the numerous folks songs of the Tsugaru District, for it is a yodel. Few songs of this kind still exist in Japan.

Yodeling is characteristic of the Ainu people who now live in parts of Hokkaidō Island. They once inhabited many of the main islands of Japan. This song comes from Aomori Prefecture, the last area of the main Japanese island where the Ainus lived before moving to Hokkaidō. The song is sung is a local dialect. Thus, "hohai" is pronounced "huhai" and is so spelled in the lyrics. A second version of the song is printed below.

Iwate and Aomori Prefectures

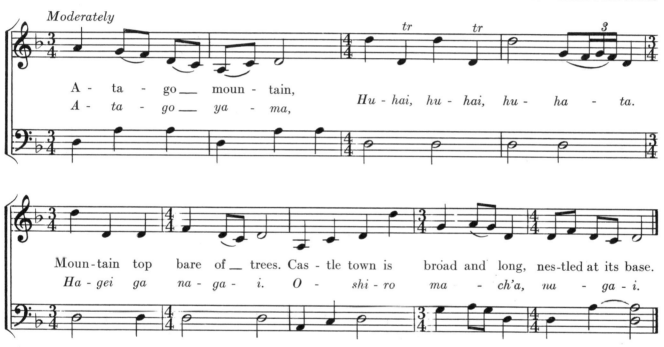

A - ta - go___ moun - tain, Hu - hai, hu - hai, hu - ha - ta.
A - ta - go___ ya - ma,

Moun-tain top bare of ___ trees. Cas - tle town is broad and long, nes-tled at its base.
Ha - gei ga na - ga - i. O - shi - ro ma - ch'a, nu - ga - i.

2. May paddies yield abundant crops!
   Hu-hai, hu-hai, hu-ha-ta.
   May the plants bend low with grain!
   Rice plants laden with heavy heads
   Will bend low with grain.

3. Our rice crop is a heavy one.
   Hu-hai, hu-hai, hu-ha-ta.
   Rice plants bend heavy with grain
   As grandmother's back is bent,
   Bent with age.

ホウハイ ブシ

青森縣

アタゴヤマ, ホウハイ, ホウハイ, ホハタ.
ハゲガ ナガイ, オシロ マチャ ナガイ.

HAKONE MOUNTAIN ROAD
(Hakone Hachiri)

This song dates from the seventeenth century. At this time a powerful warrior (shogun) family having greater power than the emperor ruled the country. As a security measure, guards were posted at the road entrances and exits of towns to inspect travelers and to search for spies.

Hakone Mountain is located in the central part of Honshu, the main island of Japan, in a region noted for its rugged scenery, plunging streams, beautiful trees, and tremendous growth of bamboo. This bamboo was used to make the canes carried by the Shoguns as a symbol of authority. The Arai River flows into the Ōi River which becomes such a furious torrent near the base of the mountain that the rock-filled stream cannot be crossed.

A mountain guide sings this song in response to a lady's request that he take her safely to a village beyond the mountain. The lyrics of the first two verses explain why he cannot fulfill her request. In the next two verses the guide expresses the idea that he is an insignificant person, less worthy than the Shogun's bamboo cane. Yet, he feels that he may yet become a worthwhile person, even though he is poor and no one cares about him. Wasn't the Otahara azalea flower unnoticed when it grew wild on Hakone Mountain? Yet, now that it has been transplanted and cultivated, it is prized highly.

Kanagawa Prefecture

We can tra- vel__ on- ly eight _____ ri* of the road,__
Ha- ko- ne _____ ha- chi - ri _____ wa

__ The Ha- ko- ne moun - tain road,__ the moun-tain road.
U - ma - de _____ mo, __ ko- su - ga.

We can - not cross the plung - ing stream,_____
Ko - su - ni ko - sa - re - nu,_____

__ O - i _____ Riv - er.
__ Ō - i - - - - - - ga - wa.

*A *ri* is about 2½ miles.

2. If there were no guard house and no Arai River,
   No Hakone guard and no wild stream,
   It would be possible to go
   Beyond the mountain.

3. I wish I were a Hakone bamboo,
   For if I were a bamboo I'd be esteemed.
   I am less worthy than the cane
   Carried by the Shogun.

4. Would that I were transplanted
   In order that I might receive respect and love.
   The transplanted azalea flower
   Now is prized highly.

ハコネ　ハチリ
ハコネ　ハチリハ　ウマデモ　コスガ,
コスニ　コサレヌ　オォイガハ .

FARAWAY ISLAND
(Entō Shinku)

Sendai lies on the northeast coast of Honshu, the main island of Japan, and Tōshima (Tō Island) lies not far beyond. To reach the island, one must cross the treacherous Ishinomaki current, one of the many dangerous currents which flow through the seas surrounding Japan.

This song tells the sad tale of a fisherman who set sail from a mainland fishing village to visit his sweetheart on a lonely island. As you sing it, duplicate the rhythm of the fisherman's laborious rowing against the wild northeast winds.

Miyagi Prefecture

Copyright 1964 by The John Day Company, Inc.

2. Ha! The sharp northeast wind blows wildly!
   It takes our sails aback and the boat stops.
   The wild, strong head winds slow our progress.
   Tōshima is still too far, far away.

3. Ha! Ten days were spent in the calm harbor.
   Struggling offshore we spent one month more,
   And now we have but one day to visit
   Tōshima where we'd hoped long to remain.

エントウ　シンク

宮城縣

ハァ！　サンジュウゴタンノ，ア，
ホヲ　マキアゲテ　ユクヨ，　センダイ，
オヤサ，　イシノ　マキ．

KOREAN FOLK SONGS

BLUE BIRD
(Parangsai)

Koreans, old and young alike, love to sing "Blue Bird," a song which tells us that the early farmers made jelly from the Indian green bean. The melody, based on three scale tones only (1, 4, 5), is easy to sing and play. To illustrate the pentatonic character of the tune, play it on the black keys of the piano — G#, C#, F#.

Koreans believe that this song is the oldest folk song known in Korea today. It originated during the Silla Dynasty (57 B.C.–935 A.D.) — the golden age of Korean history. However, American musicologists find that the 1,2,4,5,6 form of the pentatonic scale was first known in China during the Ming Dynasty (1368–1644). Anthropologists contend that the 5/4 time in which this song is written is the original form, for it is still sung that way in the interior of the country. Modern children in urban areas sometimes sing this song in 3/4 time, beginning with the third and fourth measures and ending with the first and second measures.

Blue bird, blue bird, love-ly blue bird, Do not dis-turb flow'r-ing bean plant.
Sae - ya - sae - ya, pa - rang- sae - ya, Nok- du but- te an - chi ma - ra.

2. If the flow'r falls no bean will grow.
Jelly maker'll go home in tears.

파 랑 새
새야 새야 파 랑 새야,
녹두 밭에 앉 지 마 라

HUNG TARYONG

A taryong is a joyful folk song which accompanies dancing at festivals. The weeping willow tree mentioned in this song is a famous one about which many romantic tales have been told. It stands at the corner of a three-way intersection at Samkori, Chunan, in Chungchong Pukto (Province). The three roads lead to Seoul, the nation's capital, Pusan, a great port city in the South, and Onyang Hot Springs, a resort area. Sing this song lightly and humorously, for each stanza ends with the singer's teasing his loved one a bit. (Arranged by Charity Bailey and Betty Warner Dietz.)

Chungchong Pukto Province

2. Life passes rapidly, *Hŭng! Hŭng!*
Time, stop your speeding, *Hŭng! Hŭng!*
Youth's heyday disappears,
My hair is turning white, *Hŭng! Hŭng!*
E he ya, e he ya, e he ya,
Don't you be angry! *Hŭng! Hŭng!*

흥 타 령

충청북도 민요

천안 삼거리, 흥! 흥! 능수양 버들은, 흥!흥!
제 멋에 지쳐서 휘느러 졌구나, 흥! 흥!
에 헤야, 에헤야, 에헤야,
성화가 났구나, 흥! 흥!

BELLFLOWER TARYONG
(Toraji Taryong)

This taryong describes the beauty of the bellflower and tells us that young girls dig the roots high up in the hills and take them home for food. This furnished them the opportunity to meet boys, too! Listen to the song on the recording in the back of the book.

Kangwon Province

E he ra nan da,
Chi - wa - ja cho - ta,

Life is so won - der - ful!

You make my warm heart melt, oh my sweet-heart.
Ne - ga nae - kan-jang - ŭl sŭ - ri - sal - sal ta no gin - da.

도라지 타령

강원도 민요

도라지 도라지 백도라지,
심심 산천에 백도라지.
한두 뿌리만 캐여도,
대광주리가 스리살살 다 넘는다.
에 헤야, 에 헤야, 에 헤야,
에 헤리 난다, 지와자 좋다.
네가 내 간장을 스리살살
다 녹인다.

BESIDE THE NODLE RIVER
(Nodle Kangbyon)

This sad song is very popular in Korea. The Nodle River, which is now called the Han River, flows along the south edge of Seoul, the capital of South Korea. Before the country was divided, Seoul was the capital of all Korea.

Kyonggi Province

Slowly and sadly

Weep - ing wil - low trees line the riv - er bank. Grace - ful
No - dle kang byon pom bŏ - - dle. Whi - whi

branch - es sway gent - ly in the breeze. Mer - ci - less time flows
nŭ - rŏ - jin ka - ji - e ta - ga. Mu jŏ - ng se wŏl

on like the riv - er. Time goes so quick - ly. Would that time could be de -
han hŏ - - ri - rŭl. Ching - ching tong yŏ - - na

tained by the wil - low trees. E he yo. Trust not the spring wil - lows,
mae yŏ - na bol - ka. Bom bŏ - dle do,

39

They but watch life flow-ing past like the stream. Riv - ers
Mom mi - dŭ_____ ri - - ro - da. Pu - rŭ -

flow____ cease-less - ly on thro' the ag - es for e - ons and e - ons,
rŭ - - n chŏ gi _____ chŏ - mul - man,___

Mer - ci - less time nev - er ____ stops for ____ you or me.
Hŭl - rŏ ____ hŭl - rŏ - sŏ ____ ka - no - - - ra.

2. I saw many footprints on the white sands,
   Countless footprints on the Nodle River beach.
   The footprints on the white sands of the river never remain.
   Wind and rain, how many have you erased?
   E he ya! Trust not the sand beach!
   Sands but watch life flowing past like the stream.
   Rivers flow ceaselessly on through the ages for eons and eons.
   Merciless time never stops for you or me.

3. Blue waters of the Nodle River,
   I can't trust even the water of the stream.
   How many people have ended their lives in your waters?
   How many lives have you carried away?
   E he ya! The flowing blue water!
   You should earn our trust, we should trust you.
   You should float away the sorrows of all the people,
   You should carry the sorrow of people far away.

노들 강 변

경기도 민요

노들 강변 봄 버들, 휘휘 늘어진 가지에다가,
무정 세월 한허리를, 칭칭 동여나 매어나 볼가.
에 헤요, 봄 버들도 못 민으리로다.
푸루른 저기 저 물만, 흘러 흘러서 가노라.

ARIRANG

This song, the most popular of all Korean folk songs, is one of eight "Arirangs" native to the eight provinces into which Korea was divided prior to 1896. Originating in Kyonggi Do (Province) where the Special City of Seoul is located, the song soon spread throughout the country and inspired folks in the other provinces to create their own "Arirangs." Most of these contained few modifications of the original melody or lyrics. The song took its name from Arirang Hill, a small hill in the northeastern outskirts of Seoul leading to one of the public cemeteries. Since Korea is a mountainous country, each province has its own Arirang Hill. Only the original song is called "Arirang." The others are identified by adding the name of the province, such as the "Kangwon Do Arirang" which follows.

Thomas Choonbai Park has arranged the vocal harmony of this song in the European fashion favored by modern Koreans.

Kyonggi Province

Smoothly, with a swing

A - ri - rang __ a - ri - rang __ a - ra - ri - yo. _____

You are leav-ing me to go a-way o'er A - ri - rang Hill. _____
A - ri - rang __ ko __ gae - rŭl __ no - mo - gan - da. _____

Oh, my dar-ling if you leave __ me a - lone, _____
Na - rŭl pŏ - ri - go ka - si - nŭn - nim __ ŭn, _____

May your feet __ pain you long be - fore you walk __ one mile.
Sim - ni - do __ mot __ ka __ so __ bal - byong - nan - da.

2. (Repeat first two lines.)
   Many stars sparkle high in the sky above,
   Still my heart is heavy with the sorrow your leaving brings.

3. (Repeat first two lines.)
   Tell me, is Arirang Hill bewitched?
   The more I climb, the higher it seems!

아 리 랑

경기도 민요

아리랑 아리랑 아라리요,
아리랑 고개를 넘어간다.
나를 버리고 가시는 님은
십리도 못가서 발병 난다.

KANGWON DO ARIRANG

This Arirang, like the previous one, is a sad love song. Again, a lover goes away over Arirang Hill.

This version is harmonized in fourths, the traditional manner which is favored by older people and folks in the interior of the country. Either part sung separately provides the melody of this song. You may harmonize this song in fifths or octaves to create other forms of the traditional harmony. (Vocal harmony by Thomas Choonbai Park.)

Kangwon Province

Smoothly, with swinging rhythm

Sweet ca - mel - lia flow - er, oh!___ don't bloom this ___ spring!
A - ju - kka - ri tong baek - a ___ yo - ji - ma - ra.

Your fra - - grance makes___ guile - less young girls ___ yearn for love.
San - kkol - e ___ chyŏ - nyŏ - ga tae - nan - bong nan - da.

A - ri - a - ri,___ sŭ - ri - sŭ - ri, ___ A - ra - ri - yo.
A - ri - a - ri, ___ ko - gae - rul nŏ - mo - găn - da.

You leave me so sad as you walk___ t'ward A - ri - rang Hill.
A - ri - a - ri, ___ ko - gae - rul nŏ - mo - găn - da.

2. Let me see you, let me see you, oh, my sweetheart!
   Meet me at the rendezvous house at Ajukari.
   Ariari, surisuri, arariyo.
   You leave me so sad as you walk t'ward Arirang Hill.

3. Bean flow'rs are not blooming, I wanted them so much!
   But camellias at Ajukari bloom almost too well!
   Ariari, surisuri, arariyo.
   You leave me so sad as you walk t'ward Arirang Hill.

강원도 아리랑

강원도 민요

아쥬까리 동백아 여지 마라,
산꼴에 쳐녀가 대난봉 난다.
아리아리, 스리스리, 아라리요,
아리아리 고개로 넘어간다.

SWEET SIXTEEN
(I-pal Chyŏngchyun Ka)

In Korea, as in China, marriages were arranged by parents while their children were very young. If the young boy died before he was old enough to claim his bride, the girl was considered a widow. Since women of the middle and upper classes were not allowed to remarry, some girls became widows before they had lived with their husbands. This song tells the heartbroken tale of such a young virgin widow.

Kyonggi Province

Slowly and sadly

My sad— sto-ry should be told,———— My heart— is ————
I - pal chyŏng - chyu - ne, ———— Hol - kwa - su dwe -

bro - - ken. It is too heart- break-ing, too sad,————
yŏ - - sŏ. Sŏl - um - ŭi sa - - jong - ŭl ————————

To be— a wid— ow at six - teen!
Nwi - ge - da mal - ha - rya. ————

Copyright 1964 by The John Day Company, Inc.

2. My tears are flowing so freely,
   My tears can fill the Han River.
   I sigh so deeply! I sigh enough
   To make a fluffy, floating cloud.

이 팔 청 춘 가

경기도 민요

이팔 청춘에 홀과수 되여서,

설음의 사정을 뉘게다 말하랴.

SPRINGTIME
(Yangsando)

This gay folk song probably was originated by the laborers who built Kyungbuk Palace in Seoul at the end of the Yi Dynasty, about one hundred years ago. They used it as a work song, moving rhythmically as they sang. Modern Koreans love to sing this song at festivals, picnics, and parties. They frequently accompany the song with a melodic instrument, often a violin.

Kyonggi Province

2. *E he ya!* Springtime, springtime,
   Butterflies flying joyously from flower to flower.
   They love the atmosphere of warm spring days,
   Floating on the breeze. *E he ra!*
   Life is so good, it's pleasant in springtime!
   Oh that I could fly gracefully as a butterfly!
   Springtime makes us feel so gay.

양 산 도

경기도 민요

에헤야! 봄이 왔네, 봄이 왔네,

지나간 봄철이 다시 왔네.

에헤라! 좋구나, 참 좋구나,

싫건 놀아를 보자.

각가지 화초가 참 좋구나.

NOTES ON PRONUNCIATION

There are many similarities in the pronunciation* of Chinese, Japanese, and Korean. Consonants are pronounced as in English, double consonants (bb, etc.) having a harder sound than single consonants. In general, each vowel is pronounced separately and each syllable is given equal stress (Oi = *oh-ee*). There are a few diphthongs. Pronounce as follows:

VOWELS	*DIPHTHONGS*
a . . . *ah* as in calm	ai . . . as in *ai*sle
e . . . *eh* as in fed	ei . . . as in *ei*ght
i . . . *ee* as in police	
o . . . *oh* as in told	
u . . . *oo* as in book	

Additional suggestions for pronunciation:

Chinese   ao . . . *ow* as in owl and uh . . . *u* as in but

Korean   ae . . . *a* as in at   and ŏ . . . *u* as in cup

         oe . . . *a* as in ate   ŭ   . . . *u* as in fur

Japanese kyu is pronounced as *cue.* In words such as *Tokyo,* the long *o* sound is added to the *ky* sound of *cue.*

Sometimes the following single or double consonants are sounded as syllables by themselves:

Chinese . . . *zz*   Japanese . . . *n*   Korean . . . *n* or *ng*

Many of the songs are in dialect and have been so transcribed.

* The Japanese songs are transcribed according to the Hepburn System of Romanization.
The Korean songs are transcribed according to the McCune-Reischauer System of Romanization.
The romanization of Chinese would require too many descriptive notes. Therefore, these lyrics are transcribed phonetically.

TO THE TEACHER

This is a "get acquainted" songbook. Sing the songs again and again, for Oriental tunes are unfamiliar to Western ears. Live them as you sing. Rock a baby to sleep as you croon the "Aizu Lullaby." Share the sorrow of the beautiful girl who is a widow at "Sweet Sixteen." Feel the gay abandon expressed in "The Vagabond's Song." Create a dance to the impelling rhythm of "Making Rice Cakes," a joyful festival song. The nonsense syllables (written in italics) in many of these songs roll gaily over your tongue and delight children just as the English "Whipsee deedle de dandy O!" and "Fol de rol de rol de ray" bring chuckles and requests to "sing the song just once more!" The strange melodies become familiar melodies and you hum them unconsciously. You marvel at the beauty of the five-tone scale, no longer foreign to your ears.

When written, folk songs are no longer completely authentic, for it is impossible to write in our musical notation the quarter tones, slides, and melodic embellishments sung by the native folk singer. Even the rhythmic irregularities are smoothed out somewhat in transcribing the melodies. The folk singer frequently sings the verses with different melodies, also. Compare the written songs with the recorded versions for verification. In "The Song of the Cattle Driver," for instance, you hear slightly different melodies for the several stanzas. In "The Hohai Song" you hear instrumental interludes between stanzas. Note especially the amazing yodel of the singer.

Piano accompaniments tend to change the character of the songs, for the rural folk rarely use accompaniment for their group singing. The Chinese and Japanese traditionally sing in unison and the Koreans traditionally sing harmony. Occasionally a native flute plays the melodic line and drums provide rhythm. To hear shakuhachi (Japanese native flute) accompaniment listen to "The Hohai Song."

Rural Koreans still sing the old-style harmony in fourths, fifths, and octaves, just as Europeans did in the ninth and tenth centuries. This type of harmony appears in Anglo-American music, too. The "Kangwon Do Arirang" is harmonized in this fashion. Modern urban Koreans, responding to many years of American influence, sing in the more-familiar European type of harmony, using thirds and sixths, as is illustrated in the Kyonggi Do version of "Arirang."

Teach a bit of geography, history, and sociology as you learn these songs. The background of each is given directly beneath its title. Get out a map and locate the area from which the song comes. Discuss briefly the historical information and compare the customs of these people, as revealed in the written notes and in the lyrics, with today's customs in our country.

Teach music, too.* Notice that all the songs employ the Chinese pentatonic scales. Since Chinese culture passed to Japan across the Korean peninsula about the third century A.D., it is not surprising that the folk songs of these countries are based on Chinese scales.

To preserve the original flavor of these songs, accompany them with recorders or song bells and add the rhythm of drums, finger cymbals, or rattles. For the Chinese and Japanese songs, play only the melody in unison or at the octave. For the Korean songs, play the melody line with one recorder and the harmony line (ancient or modern) with another. You can easily arrange any of the Korean songs in traditional harmony by adding a parallel melodic line at the fourth or the fifth — even if you are what you conceive to be a "musical illiterate."

The major purpose of this book is to encourage children and adults to sing with joy the music of three Oriental countries. Therefore, do not stress the technicalities of the music to a point where enjoyment is impaired. Songs are to be sung and loved!

* See Reference Material for Teaching Music.

Interest in these folk songs is heightened by attention to the meter in which they are written, the phrasing, and the varied types of Chinese pentatonic scales represented. Most of the Chinese and Japanese songs are written in duple meter — 2/4 or 4/4 time — and most of the Korean songs are written in triple meter — 3/4 or 6/8 time. While 6/8 time often gives the "feel" of duple meter (accents on *one* and *four*), "Hung Taryong" and "Sweet Sixteen" both are sung slowly in a waltz rhythm. The musically trained reader will be sensitive, also, to the varied phrasing patterns in these songs. Some are phrased regularly, some most irregularly.

All but four of the songs use the most common of the Chinese pentatonic scales, one which is said to have been identified by a historian of the second century B.C.* This scale is based on the 1st, 2nd, 3rd, 5th, and 6th tones of the scale. If a song is written in either of the two ways illustrated on the left, it may be played on the black keys of the piano or on the upper row of bars on the song bells by raising or lowering the tones one-half step as illustrated on the right. All of the songs may be transposed into one of these two keys for purposes of demonstration but they may then become too high or too low for comfortable singing.

"Cool Breezes" adds one scale tone to those above — the 7th. There are two possible explanations for this. Either the melody has become acculturated or the song may employ the ancient Chou Dynasty scale which was the principal scale from 1116 B.C. to the end of the Sung Dynasty (thirteenth century A.D.). However, the song makes use of only one tone in addition to the original five and the ancient scale shows the occasional use of two tones — the 4th and the 7th.

Three of the songs employ later scales based on the 1st, 2nd, 4th, 5th, and 6th tones of the scale rather than the 1-2-3-5-6 mode described earlier. "Blue Bird" uses only three tones of this scale — the 1st, 4th, and 5th. The "Song of the Cattle Driver" uses the entire scale (in the key of B minor). This scale became popular during the Ming Dynasty (1368–1644).

Another seven-tone scale appeared during the Ch'ing Dynasty (1644–1912) but this was based on the 1-2-4-5-6 pentatonic scale with the occasional use of 3 and 7. "Faraway Island" appears to be based on this scale.

Three of the songs show European influence. The "Song of the Three 'Nots'" (Chinese) has acquired an A♯ which is not in the original mode. "Making Rice Cakes" (Japanese), which is written in the ancient 1-2-3-5-6 scale, shows acculturation in its major-minor-major form. "Arirang" (Korean) shows no outside influences in its original melody but has been harmonized in the European fashion now favored by urban Koreans.

* Information about Chinese scales is from the Fifth Edition of *Grove's Dictionary of Music and Musicians*, edited by Eric Bloom.

This list identifies the songs that may be played on the black keys of the piano in their present form:*

CHINESE
Bad Faith .... ♭
Frogs .... ♭
Gently Flowing Stream ...... ♭
Song of the Three "Nots" ..... ♭
Why Don't You Come
    Home? .... ♭

JAPANESE
Hakone Mountain Road ..... ♭
Hohai Song .... ♯
Sea Gulls Offshore .... ♭

KOREAN
Arirang (melody only) .... ♭
Bell Flower Taryong .... ♯
Beside the Nodle River ...... ♯
Blue Bird .... ♯
Hung Taryong .... ♭
Springtime .... ♭
Sweet Sixteen .... ♭

* Lower scale tones ½ tone, or flat the keys ... ♭
  Raise scale tones ½ tone, or sharp the keys ... ♯

SONGBOOKS AND RECORDS

BOOKS

Children's Songs from Japan, by Florence White and Kazuo Aki-
  yama. New York: Edward B. Marks Music Corporation, 1960.

East-West Songs. Delaware, Ohio: Cooperative Recreation Service,
  Incorporated, 1960.†

Flower Drum and Other Chinese Songs, by Chin-Hein Yao Chen
  and Shi-Hsiang Chen. New York: The John Day Company,
  1943.

Sampler of Japanese Songs. Delaware, Ohio: Cooperative Recreation Service, Incorporated, 1958. Companion recording, 10″ L.P.

Swing High: Korean Folk Recreation. Delaware, Ohio: Cooperative Recreation Service, Incorporated, 1954.

RECORDS

Folk and Classical Music of Korea. Folkways. 12″ L.P.

Folk Music of Japan. Folkways Records. 12″ L.P.

Folk Songs of Japan and Korea. The recording in this book.

Music of Asia, George List, Editor, Indiana University Archives of
  Folk and Primitive Music. Indiana Audio-Visual Center, 1964.
  2 12″ L.P., brochure.

Traditional Folk Songs of East Japan. Folkways. 12″ L.P.

Traditional Folk Songs of West Japan. Folkways. 12″ L.P.

*World Library of Folk and Primitive Music: Japan, the Ryukyus,
  Formosa, and Korea.* Columbia. 12″ L.P.

† The Cooperative Recreation Service has many small songbooks for sale at 25¢ and 30¢.
  Some books have companion recordings, ranging in price from $1.00 to $3.00.

About the Editors

BETTY WARNER DIETZ, an assistant professor at Brooklyn College, has long felt the value of music in bringing together people of different cultures and colors, and has taken a special interest in the music of the Orient since her service as a member of the American Education Mission to Korea in 1952–53. A graduate of Northwestern University, she received her doctorate in education at New York University. She has taught in public schools in Scarsdale, New York, New Orleans, and Deerfield, Illinois, and since 1950 at Brooklyn College. Music has always played a prominent part in her activities.

Besides her service in Korea, she has studied school systems in Japan, the Philippines, Thailand, Pakistan, India, Turkey, and several European nations. She was for a time educational consultant to the American-Korean Foundation. She has written book reviews and articles in *School Library Journal, Journal of Teacher Education, Childhood Education,* etc.

Dr. Dietz has recently completed a manuscript on the musical instruments of Africa which is being prepared for publication.

THOMAS CHOONBAI PARK is a Korean educator, also specializing in music, who is now an associate professor at Florida Memorial College in St. Augustine, Florida. The son of a mathematics professor, he attended secondary school and college in Seoul, Korea, and taught for fifteen years in Korean elementary schools and at the College of Education of Seoul National University. He came to the United States in 1956 and received his doctorate in education from the University of Florida in 1961.

Dr. Park is the author of a music textbook for elementary schools published in Korea.